Yo

Really glad you
enjoyed it - I've
had a great time
in Leeds and
really really enjoyed
the bands too!
I'll be back, as
Anna said...
           All the best,

           RJ

CW00735493

GERMLINE

Richard Tyrone Jones was born in 1980 in the
West Midlands. He read History at King's College,
Cambridge and now works in London as a writer,
educator, live literature promoter and host of the
popular 'Utter!' spoken word events, writing group and
MisGuided tours. His work has been published in a
number of periodicals and he has read for most of the
major live poetry series in the UK. This compendium of
poetry, fiction and art is his first publication.

GERMLINE

**Richard
Tyrone
Jones**

Germline

Copyright Richard Tyrone Jones 2009

The right of Richard Tyrone Jones to be identified as the author of this work has been asserted in accordance with the Copyright, Designs and Patents Act 1988.

ISBN: 978-0-9554989-2-3

A CIP record for this title is available from the British Library.

All rights reserved. No part of this publication may be reproduced, stored in a retrieval system, or transmitted at any time or by any means electronic, mechanical, photocopying, recording or otherwise without prior permission of the copyright holder.

Published by Vintage Poison Press.

Printed in Constantia, Cambria and UNION AGROCHEM in the UK by Cromwell Press Group.

Richard Tyrone Jones's work has previously appeared in: *Brittle Star, The Delinquent, The Fix, Fuselit, Irk, Krax, litro, The London Magazine,* Oxfam's *Poems for a Better Future, Rising, Stop Me and Buy One, Tales of the Decongested Vol II, Trespass,* and on the-errorist.com and metaroar.com. Thanks to all their editors.

Further information, appearances, MP3s and blog can be found at www.myspace.com/richardtyronejones as well as Facebook. All comments and enquiries gratefully received at richardtyronejones@gmail.com

Genome

Adenine

Geological child   12
The invitation   14
Identity theft   15
Kick racism out of football   16
Unwieldy metaphor   17
The re-match   16
Scratch a liberal   17
To get to the other side   20
Pile-up   21
Advice you never asked for   22
An uncle's advice   24
Just to confirm   25
Recycling the Chinrezig sand mandala   27
Parable   28
Polar conquest   29
Henry Rollins   30
And from a serene night sky   32
Visiting time   33
Richard Dawkins   35
Unborn children   36
Critical switch   37
Germline   38
Into the cattle trucks   40
Act of will   42
My bench   43

Cytosine

Altruism	46
The wheel-clamper	46
Apres moi, le deluge	47
Toiletries	47
Tower of bones	48
Departure lounge	50
Boundary violation	53
Happy new year	56

Guanine

Receipts	60
Rodent triangle	61

Tartrazine

If two Hollywood icons...	64
The promise	64
God's crap Christmas	64
The celery seller's story	65
Verruca	66
Look after 'em	67
Duck camp	68
Parental Advisory: Explicit Limericks	70
Shit poem	72

Notes

Adenine

Geological child

In the false sunset when eyes dip beneath the clouds,
in the Neolithic age when man dozes into the present,

I, aged six and drunk - on books and dinosaurs alone -
(don't give kids booze at the dinner table; they don't *need* it)
imagined things more interesting than I would shortly dream
(I dreamt a lion bit my head off. Every night.)
The dark void voyage at the edge of the bed,
the chasm to underneath it,
was a layered ladder of geological rungs.
Copied from a book without use of crayon,
eternity transplanted to empty space in miniature maquette.

In the first layer, one inch of bedspace, lay the ice age,
and if I dipped my fingertip in, it would come back
covered with frost. Another inch inches down,
the second segment of my finger freezes whilst the tip is nipped
by a sabre tooth tingle I drag down to thaw in Miocene.
Licked by a giant sloth,
charged by a giant elk,
Volkswagen parade of armadillos rumble by on a grazed-down
highway as my infant hand burrows down through their Earth
to the next underworld that time has remembered, down –
like reaching down a Lilliputian lift shaft to pluck Adam & Eve
from the ground,
each door pings on a different office of administrating dinosaurs,
photocopying, cross-referencing their own fossils,
acting as their own ID. Time
to file.

A splash of water – wet ring period stretching up my arm
as it reaches to the bottom of this time-sea bed:
the Flood.
My godfearing fingers stretch antediluvian -
and on to the bottom, unbearable transitory thin paper white
heat layer of volcanic still-cooling Earth, forge of the godhead
imaginative of infancy. Is this Alpha my journey's end?

I arm further, expecting Genesis,
through light into darkness, Fall, and feathers,
brush the angel wings – I hit carpet.
My reach has grown since last time.

The invitation

'Dear _____,' it read,
'I'm inviting you to a party.
I'm not telling you where it is,
when, or how to get there,
but you can't say you haven't been
invited.'

I am still on good terms with my ex.

Identity theft

When someone stole my identity
(I was too tight to buy a shredder)
they went bungee jumping on safari in Africa,
got stoned in the 'dam, coked up in Venezuela,
went to The End on all the nights I couldn't get anyone to go to,
bought a house then sold it again,
married a Russian girl then divorced her,
patronised a high-class brothel, joined a gym
and actually went more than once.
Chartered a plane to chase an eclipse,
bought a load of top-quality DJ equipment, used it,
went on holiday to Samarkand, rented a jeep and a hospice,
sponsored a forest to offset his carbon footprint –
burnt it down, bought another further North,
bankrolled a worthwhile arthouse film
and less excitingly, took time off to finally complete my MA.

I expect it was the doing of my successful identical twin
merely rubbing in how little I've achieved compared to him
as I surmised when all the invoices had arrived at my house
but not one penny had gone missing from my account.

Kick racism out of football

If I were a black player in the 1970s
and someone threw a banana at me,
I like to think I'd shrug nonchalantly,
pick it up, peel it,
consume it at a leisurely pace, as if to say

'I'll take your bigotry and I'll eat it,
digest it, shit it back out my black arse,
because I'm bigger than your prejudice,
for everyone on Earth eats bananas
as every race on Earth evolved from apes.'

However, they then might throw two, three,
four bananas, and having eaten one
I'd have to eat them all, and letting in
a goal while I'm busy eating bananas in the cause of racial equality
might not make me a good ambassador for the game.

Yes, I'd probably ignore the bananas.
But if I were an unpopular ref
I'd definitely think 'fuck it', pocket
the coins they threw at my head.
Unless of course I was Jewish.

Or unconscious.

Unwieldy metaphor

One drunk night an unwieldy metaphor met our bonnet
halfway between the sublime and the ridiculous.
Like an injured mongrel pup I scooped it up, took it home with us.

I'd find it a place. Strained to lever it into the back
seat of a joke, but it snapped the axles.
I lugged it to the battlefield, where it misfired.

Tried to offer it the missus in a chocolate-covered sonnet;
it cracked the tip of an iceberg tooth.
Dumped it overboard, but it returned with the tide.

Fired it to the moon from where it shone straight back at me;
on E-bay and in Loot it proved an uncommon currency.

Eventually, in a heaving rucksack, it lurched behind
me to an open mic, a fat, obstreperous child,
where some arch punter called it the most contrived metaphor

for an unwieldy metaphor that he had ever heard,
that it was 'awful, in both senses of the word;
I like it', he insisted, seeming only slightly snide.

Before he could backpedal, 'You can have it' fled my mouth,
and yapping after it, my self, feeling much the better for it.

The re-match

The wind blew to the sun: 'Hey, I
bet you all the leaves on the trees
that I can get that man in the street's coat off faster
than you can.' 'You never learn!' said the sun.
'The bet is on, my friend. You're all bluster.'

The sun went first, strained with all his might,
almost supernovaed, the man sweated and tottered but
the coat stayed on. 'Your turn', panted the sun.
The wind idly cracked its whip,
the bloke's coat smoothly surfed off on its sine wave.

Said the sun: 'You chiseller,
you knew he'd got no arms, didn't you?'

Scratch a liberal

They say 'Scratch a liberal, you'll find a fascist'.
But scratch a fascist, you'll find a communist,
scratch a communist, you'll find an anarchist,
scratch an anarchist, you'll find a feudalist,
scratch a feudalist, you'll find a Roman republican,
scratch a Roman republican, you'll find a democrat
though they will be *incredibly* tiny.

To get to the other side

Erin, fifteen, pride of the next door neighbours
was pretty, clever, so they reported, colour-blind.
Hemmed into tunnel vision by parked vans,
the letter in her hand and a dutiful nature
it was as if she was hit by the middle of the road.

Her Mum turned round to see her crumple.
Ours, when she heard, loosed the salt-water sluices of suburbia.
My sister and I raced the house, closing curtains,
flicking the local paper for the news, more excited than
upset, ran past it without looking; it had made page one.

It confirmed her father in his upright ways.
He'd scold the kids who played in his dried-up drain.
A couple of years later he was talking to Mum outside
when I joined them, and the door blew shut behind.
He lurched himself over our rusted gate to let us in the back.

I assumed that adults would put the latch on after such an incident,
(it's what I would have done had I been one, but I wasn't so I didn't)
thus the door blew shut again. Incredulous, more offended that this
redheaded whelp in NHS specs had *not* done this on purpose
than suspicious that he had, our neighbour cursed his lot.

And even now, both you and he, if you're anything like me,
will still fail to judge clearly the distance, in every child's mistakes,
between incompetence, impulsiveness, and the deepest intent.
And even now, I forget to check both ways.

Pile-up

The accident black spot ate teenagers and excreted urban myths.
You'll have heard the one about the kids who
drunk, skidded into it, leapt
through the windscreen more
grudgingly graceful than showroom dummies,
died and gave birth to a bed of flowers.

One week later, two more kids of the same age
took the same corner at the
same speed, just as drunk,
hit it at the same angle, same make of car but survived for the
impact was cushioned by the
snowdrift of flowers, cards and stuffed toys piled high.

Another week later, once the news had done its rounds,
a crazy man from Aberdeen drove full pelt into it,
bollards breaking neck as the molar doth a twiglet,
wearing no seatbelt, no airbag, nothing but a
full-size, top-to-toe
teddy bear suit.

Advice you never asked for

Ok. If work isn't, or the self-help tripe you've read already hasn't,
try this. Avoid duty if it seems like duty. Pleasure is mostly
spontaneous, isn't it? If it wears a badge saying 'duty', if it stinks
like duty, it's obligation, especially if it markets itself as leisure.

The number one piece of advice I could give you is: avoid poems
that tell you how to live your life. Even if they're right.
If you're doing what you're told
you're doing something wrong.

Live thrives on plurality. Two turtles on a whale,
the glorious biodiversity of clichés! Grow your own
but don't get stoned on them, just nicely high; keep an eye
on your wing mirrors. It's better to machete
a path through the jungle
than to tunnel underground. Moles burrow. They eat worms.

Keep your mind messy and your room tidy,
so that when you lose your mind you know where to find it.

The big themes lie in the minutiae. Growing old is still
growing. Youth glimmers in the dark because memory
is a dirt-filter, it pans for gold in the toilets of the past.
Remember that next time you're knee-deep. Never turn
down a shag. Sex; threesomes don't exist. Maybe you should
try prostitution once, if only to dispel any literary myths.
In confidence:
sex *is* confidence.

NEVER eat fast food from a place that displays a smiling cartoon
image of the animal whose meat it sells – that's just wrong.

Careers? What's to say – you already know they're just a means to
an end – your own. Though a fag break is a firebreak, redundancy
might form a more than convenient fire exit.

Family? Borrow some first. Collect more mistakes to learn from.
Your parents' might not be fucked-up *enough*.

Don't worry about worry – now we have Outlook
and Post-its for that.

Taking a risk is different from gambling. All Tories are bastards
but that doesn't mean they're not amusing company. Find a
diary which fits snugly in the pocket. Always carry plenty of water
and a slim volume. Remember anyone's advice is only ever
a route-map to where *they* are. And never give it; never give advice.
People only resent you for it. *Especially* when it's right.

An uncle's advice

'Richard. Never trust anyone with missing teeth. Because
if they can't be trusted with their *own teeth*
what can you trust them with? And never employ
fat people; they don't *do* anything,
that's why they're fat.

'And get yourself a woman who can open a bottle of beer
with her pelvic floor muscles, not
in order to actually open a beer bottle with, you understand,
I'm not being sexist,
quite the contrary, in fact. If a woman's not prepared to develop
the seat of her sexuality to become more than a passive
participant in the act of procreation, then she herself
is not a proper feminist.'

I was about to tell him: 'I'm seven, still
stranded at the anally-fixated stage of development,
finding 'poo' and 'bum' hilarious, and as such not yet ready for
your latter piece of advice', but he'd already moved onto
which insects are the most camp.

Just to confirm

I feel like two fat men fighting in a culvert.
Hose me down, fetch emetics! I need to be cleansed.
Pull an old shirt out of the wardrobe, say to yourself
'I'll never wear this again,' then don it just to spite yourself.
That's the sort of thing *you* do!

Terror descends again, as sure as nightfall
in which ghosts are slightly translucent lies
searching for a believer. They whisper: 'Imagine,
one day no-one will drink tea,'
but the mirror isn't dirty, this world is.

Reality hath bad sound quality, and
as I conjure the relevant footnotes that lie in the wavelengths
we cannot hear, cannot see, cannot feel,
in waggle-dance subtexts, misaligned Xeroxes,
I feel like an only Gog.

Transsexuals are people who found one puberty
not traumatic enough. Racists are evil
because they restrict their own customer base.
'That's not a synth, it's a kazoo,
are you trying to out-subgenre me?'

Feel my abstraction; it is palpable.
My pink wit may seem meager but remember;
9/10ths of it is antimatter. The voices state:
'At home, when white people can't hear them,
they all speak the Queen's English and chuckle at you.'

Gods are ideas with ideas of their own:
'Either the chorus are part of me, in which case I am a god
or they are not, but then I'm mortal.' Which is worse?
My heartbeast may control that music and I can't work out if it wants
to leap out of me or wants me to leap into itself.

But why turn the rib into a woman when, with it removed,
Adam could happily suck himself off?
I take no pleasure in my perversions apart from
the satisfaction of knowing I'm a pervert.
Does that make me a pervert, or not at all?

Recycling the Chinrezig sand mandala

Will we gain arcane wisdom in this art gallery cellar,
or just calm after literary exertion in hot weather?
Om mani padme hum, hail to the jewel in the lotus,
a refrain not so calming that two toddlers can't start raving.

The gaffer monk first scoops the gods from their dwellings
then sweeps up the mineral tapestry, outside-in, clockwise,
a withering pie chart of enlightenment; Pac-Man dies
or ascends to the next level, a crushed rainbow in the middle.

The mandala is doled out in party bags for all those present
though it's supposed to be dissolved in running water
so it reaches all corners of the Earth. Yet given the audience's
international nature, this method may prove quicker.

So if, in a Great Plains river, you glimpse a lapis lazuli glimmer,
or pick a grain of crushed marble from duller sand,
it was once part of a great – well, highly intricate – work of art
and will be once again. Me? I've still got two bags.

Parable

I met a tramp, who asked for food.
I had some yoghurt and a spoon.
She asked for the yoghurt,
I said 'Forget it.

'I keep the yoghurt and you have the spoon.
This way both of us go hungry
but both of us will get a story
to tell our grandchildren.

'Except neither of us will have any, probably
because you are a junky
and I am a shit.

With a yoghurty chin.'

Polar conquest

Woke up one morning in a standing position

(he lashed himself to a runner beanpole so as not to heed

the genetic failure-sirens who might lure him back to bed)

only to find his shadow had strapped itself down

with that taut catgut, regret; he strained, was clamped.

But he had loverstopaint empirestocreate arttodestroy!

It was only by six months of careful construction

of an encircling lattice of stage lamps

to illuminate his every plane wherever he walked

and another six months' weight training so he could lift it

that he could stagger to the street

melting snow and scorching foliage wherever he went,

salting water tables with his own nude sweat.

'Behold!' he gasped, 'O ye medical establishment,

I am cured!'

Henry Rollins

One day, Henry Rollins decided to hang himself
before decrepitude unmanned him. However,
the muscular girth of his tree-trunk neck left him pedaling air
for three hours. Before death, he had time to reflect,

concluding 'Liar' had been the Rollins band's only good number,
that his role in 'Johnny Mnemonic' had been misguided,
and cameos in 'Heat' and 'Lost Highway' unmemorable.
How his visits to maimed GIs had prolonged the war he hated,

how his muscles had formed a barrier as much as they had armour,
that perhaps he should have punched himself out of the closet,
that he'd secretly quite liked some shitty rave music,
that he didn't *always* have to sing like a sore-throated auctioneer

and how he really should have used a hawser.
Yet I suspected lack of oxygen had made him over-critical
and 'I always found you quite affable, myself'
was what I whispered in his ears as his lips turned tattoo-blue.

And from a serene night sky

the men leapt
in their millions
screaming from each star
aflame, a noose around each neck,
rope unravelling from the stellar windows
a cosmic stunt
hoping just
to reach
the Earth
in death
but stopped
short
ropes
taut
necks snapped,
flames extinguished by the drop,
each dangling, pendulous, smouldering,
one foot from the planet
the skies revolve around.

And will we dare to climb those ropes ourselves
when we've cut that harvest down?

Visiting time

This skeletal Michael Finnegan in a gown is
all time's winds have left of old Gran.
Sharon Stone nappy flash, water retention
has inverted her legs: thigh-like-calves, veal-calf thighs.
It's like that film, Memento, you remember,
but with just the one death.
Her memory's camera zooms towards her birth,
the film's end.

Every five minutes, a new time traveller
teleports into her body, the pod, from '68, '67, '65
and we explain it all again, 'what year is this?'
Role-playing: I'm her nephew, son-in-law, sisters are daughters,
she's got to see her dad. Playing happy families
the old maid shuffles the pack.
The songs she sings are from the war.
Her vision's gone. Can't see past 1944.

Can't even watch TV. Even if she could,
at three pounds per day they're all turned, off and to the wall,
neglected patients. These screens fade to white dots, leaving
only an afterimage pressed on the retina,
a song stuck in the memory of those about to leave;
repeats, all just repeats.

Visiting time is over.

Richard Dawkins

'We can, then, with complete confidence, reject the third of our three hypotheses, the bonkers one.'

– Dawkins, The Ancestor's Tale.

One day, Richard Dawkins was taking his wife up the arsehole.
Mid-thrust, he halted, mouthing:
'What evolutionary purpose does *this* serve?'
Well, he couldn't get hard again after that,
and his wife had to finish herself off.

Unborn children

Those unborn children are making a racket again
Banging their hands on the luxury biscuit tin
Chanting 'We would've saved your relationship'
'We would've saved your relationship'

Even though we're still together.
It must be them who've been stealing all the chocolates
They must be the reason I feel too tired to do it
They must've been behind that tumour that ate my prostate

Jumping up and down in the unconverted attic
Banging all their little heads against its walls of rubber
Ring-a-ring-a-rosing round that old upended anchor
Playing Mummies and Daddies themselves in ever-increasing panic

I had the supple wrists of a juggler
but now they're gone
You kept your figure another decade
never passed it on

We can't discern their number, though I suspect one has one leg.
Those unborn children are making a racket again
We'll have to put them up for adoption
by the couple that never even asked each other out.

Critical switch

Domitian, A.D. 73

I have dismissed the slaves. There shall be present
but six. My wife, myself, a mute midwife,
a doctor on the cusp of senescence,
my heir, and the child who will adopt his life.

For court boils toward the point of eruption
hemlock grows in each uncle's eyes,
eagled generals, eager for adoption
hide daggers in every cup of wine.

Thus night's purple shift will lift on a safe home
where he'll grow to tend goats, a Sabine peon,
turn fireman in some dank suburb of Rome
or stevedore in Herculaneum;

but I shall never know, nor see my son
lest he return, revenge what we have done.

Germline

'Try to imagine the kind of things you would want to know if you had been conceived using donated sperm.'

So, happy eighteenth, you've found out you're donated!
(Although if your parents are both lesbians, you probably
realised this already, unless my seed has sired an imbecile.)
And so you're curious to know a little more about me. Well,
here we are, all facts correct at time of going to press, ha ha –
just my little joke there. I have a good sense of humour... This is
like writing a singles ad on a website, except that the ultimate
object of that exercise has already been achieved.

I have a degree from Cambridge, which is probably why your
parents (and I want you to know that some of the best friends
I've ever misguidedly tried to pull are lesbians) chose me,
despite my minority hair. I want you to know that I have done
absolutely nothing with my degree and that they are incredibly
overrated. I'd go straight to work if I were you and if you don't,
no, I'm not contributing to your tuition fees. But then if I still
need to masturbate for cash aged twenty-seven, I'm hardly
going to be in a position to, am I?

Perhaps you are merely the product of my enthusiasm for
recycling. I recycle my food waste, plastic, paper and metal, I've
looked into a system whereby my shit will heat my house, I
grow my hair really long then sell it to a wig-maker, and feared
only my seed was being wasted; for even Tower Hamlets do not
recycle jism.

I am a keen cyclist because I hate public transport.
I hate public transport because I hate the public.
'The public' includes girls, which is why I am here.
This is how curmudgeons breed. Which is why you are here.

So though I wish you all the best, I could have up to nine other children (plus siblings, if requested) so if I do forget your name I apologise in advance. I believe in Darwinism and feared I would never get another girlfriend, which grew into fearing I'd never be a father, that my genome would go unreplicated. Then I saw an evolutionary loophole - and I stuck my pink future in it. I want you to know I lied about absolutely nothing on my medical statement.

So if I haven't utterly disappointed you with my honesty so far, please do get in touch. In fact, please do get in touch anyway, as on second thoughts I am probably by now an incredibly lonely old man. And as we recognise each other's phenotypes across the lunchtime restaurant, and flinch, then recompose ourselves to embrace, shake hands, or just glower at each other judgmentally over tapas, I don't mind if you don't feel like calling me 'Dad'. Just please don't, however accurate it may be, call out 'Wanker!'

Into the cattle trucks

'Extermination must be put on a scientific basis if it is ever to be carried out humanely and apologetically as well as thoroughly.'
                                                    - George Bernard Shaw

People who stop abruptly in the middle of the street
Girls whose labels stick up at the back
Old men who would not say their prayers
Fussy eaters, 'allergic to rat'.

They who tried to fool us by wearing contact lenses
People who used to queue for ATMs *across* the pavement
Women with double-buggies, men with cystitis
Dem yoots who refused to belt up their trousers

Not Ray Mears.

Everybody now
We were running out of food,
we were running out of water
but everything we did, we did
that you might live, my daughter

Those whose moles spelt words in Arabic
Those who insisted on impractical clothes
Those whose surnames began with an X
It wasn't planned on a racist basis, but that was the letter
the ouija board chose

They who defied us by helping those in hiding
They who lacked the moral fibre to help those in hiding
Those in hiding
(Except the ones we couldn't find, obviously
- we gave them an amnesty).

Yo DJ bring that beat back
It was through their loss
that your future was won
so no pressure, but
make the most of it, my son

The epileptic, the diabetic,
The junkies and the anorexic
(But I let one go every ten days!)
Those who let one go every ten days

The proud, the meek, the old, the weak,
The homeless, the menopausal,
The ones who just got in the way of reprisals,
Those with less than twenty-one teeth.

Unh, unh, a little louder
You're probably wondering, my children,
what we're telling you all this now for.
It's so you won't resist when our ticket,
as it must do, drops through our door.

Act of will

It's nothing religious, but after I die

don't siphon my blood into an anaemic
don't butcher my legs for an anaconda's chops
if the heart still roars, don't donate it to a coward
don't take my penis down the charity shop

don't cut out my brain and stick it on top of one of those autistic
kids with skyscraper heads you're building in order to reconcile
relativity theory with quantum mechanics, reconstitute the Ur-
language or pen the Great American Novel
don't donate my eyes to blind voyeurs
don't use my anal sphincter for the airlock on a mouse's spaceship
don't string your pain-piano with my nerves

'Cos I'm coming back, you fuckers, first one to come back -
with a real estate portfolio to make the pharaohs blush.

My bench

Richard Tyrone Jones

1980 – 2038

He was a shit

TRAMPS GET PRIORITY.

Cytosine

Altruism

The city boss trumpeted his £100m giveaway. 'I'm giving away £100m to charity,' his press release read, 'not because I *care* about the donkey sanctuary, but purely in order to buy good press.' Inevitably, from most quarters, opprobrium was heaped upon him for such a cynical attitude, but in the circles that mattered he was applauded for acknowledging the selfish nature of altruism and thus, in the eyes of business, validating it. In his wake, corporate donations to charity tripled.

The wheel-clamper

Boris worked for a wheel-clamping company which went bust. However, in the confusion of liquidation, he was able to acquire a complete set of tools for the removal of wheel clamps. He now parks his van in restricted areas, gets it clamped, then removes the clamps himself with his wheel clamp removal tools. He now has almost enough wheel clamps to start his own wheel-clamping business. As well as being able to park wherever he likes.

Apres moi, le deluge

Yes, I manned the barricades in '68. I can't remember now what exactly I thought I was, politically, but I can remember that, like the rest, I hated de Gaulle and hate him still. This was why, some years later, I had his face tattooed on my wife's back, so that when we were doing it doggy style I could stare at his face with venomous disgust until my wife's face achieved orgasm, then turn her over and finally reach my climax gazing into her much more feminine visage. I always remember his portentous statement, 'apres moi, le deluge' as I pop all over my wife's jubblies.... It may not have been through dialectical materialism, but I have defeated him.

Toiletries

The couple were drawn together by their mutual passion for reading on the toilet. They shared an extensive library (in the toilet), where each book had at least two post-it notes sticking out of it, one green, one pink, to mark their respective places. In fact they'd first met at a party, where he had been queuing for half an hour outside the toilet because she was on it, reading Edgar Allan Poe. His chat-up line, 'Has your arse dried yet?' worked.

Eventually they were driven out of the house they shared with five others, for obvious reasons, and got a place of their own, where they installed two toilets, side by side, on which they could sit and shit and read together, to their hearts', minds' and bottoms' content.

Tower of bones

The Sultan wanted a tower made of bones, to scorn the death of his beloved. No-one, therefore, would be killed in its construction. Not directly. He took out life insurance on behalf of each of his subjects – to be paid out even to suicides, the number of which trebled. As he owned all the land in his kingdom not possessed by the mosques, all buried bones were unearthed from unhallowed ground and stockpiled. He put in place a comprehensive canopy of environmental protection edicts, to camouflage a provision prohibiting cremations. Further stratagems he adopted. Laws were passed to ensure all xylophones were to be henceforth fashioned from wood – his Grand Vizier closed loopholes relating to glockenspiels. Expeditions were made to the interior, to the elephant graveyards. Pachyderm domes would adorn the arches.

Infant skulls made doorknockers hinged by biting on an adult mandible, every four ribs formed an elliptical window. Two hip bones sat as bay seats beneath each. Thighs became bricks and ribs beams (as they had previously been). Fingers formed brackets, elbows hinged doors. Backbones by the hundred tacked together made the supporting columns. Robust remains of the young bore those of the old, supporting walls hefting inferior interior interiors. Writers' teeth chattered once more as the keys to the tower's typewriters. Ossified thumbs, opposable again, inserted for entrance to curled fist locks. Click. Echoes. For no one would live here but the dead, who clambered on over each other up their own stairs as banisters constructed from forearms, the hands at each end clasping tightly the elbow of the next, pulled each other up to roofs cobbled with penitent knees. One thousand and one stairs, the staircase ran up one thousand and one feet on one thousand and one thighs of five hundred and one knights, the last of whom had been one-legged.

Needless to say, the Sultan of whom we speak never saw his skeletal tower completed. His bones, with others added to splint his osteoporotic frame, built a throne for his successor, his infant son, to seat his own temporarily-befleshed endoskeleton on. On the eve of his twenty-first birthday, and coming of age, the Crown Protector, the Grand Vizier, symbolically completed the building with the removal of his own knee to head the last bolt on its massive gate. At dawn, the prince would be raised on the edifice of his father's triumphs and his mother's memory and, in so doing, become sultan.

Yet, as blue ink spilt onto the East, a shifting creaking was heard throughout the kingdom. Petrified, the prince ran to the window which looked out from the old palace onto the tower, fearful that the work that had salvaged the product of thousands of lifetimes was to fall. His thoughts were of the powdered skulls of its failed architects buttressing the foundations of its successor. Rocking from the balls of his feet to his toes, he impatiently hummed till the sashes were thrown back for him. The ziggurat of purest white had turned pink, the gate to death closed tight by cherry lips, the crumbling tower growing tight in sinew, its staircases, halls and corridors rasping with the first sweat of a monumental sigh.

Departure lounge

The modern day extermination camp I work at is not called an Extermination camp but a 'Departure lounge,' which is both more and less than it is, or at least, what I suspect it is, there being no proof. It is 100% effective, designed by Marketing professionals. I am a Customer Services Officer. I guide the new departures past the deck where we relieve them of their luggage, down the right aisles to the right departure lounges where we keep them waiting with complimentary coffee and whereby we separate them from the rest of each influx.

Like I say, I only suspect that when they finally mount the escalators into the blinding white light they are killed. I only suspect that it is painless. I know the couples that meet at the sterile, clean and happy Arrivals lounge all departures must pass by on their way are actors who meet again and again, but that is, even for staff, a different and therefore restricted area so we may not talk to these people and confirm, or unconfirm, what I suspect. Different sections of staff enter by different doors, eat in different canteens. Only the departures see the other staff's faces, though we sometimes hear their voices. No-one sees machines or bodies. There may even be more staff after me to be the last to see them. Not knowing that is the one blank bullet in the firing squad's guns, enables the plausible denial of an implausible process. Like I say, I only suspect. Why would you believe? Why would you want to believe?

Here comes a Chinese girl, confused and wary, laden down with bumbag, camera bag, two rucksacks, all in the same beige goretex. She should have deposited them before the last set of those pull-out cordons that fling themselves back into their freestanding black columns as soon as you let them go, if you do not fix them to the next black column. I should politely explain to her in my foreign tongue that she cannot take them with her. But I still possess some vestiges of compassion and I let her ascend the escalators peacefully. It is the least I can do for her. We *must* have enough digital cameras already.

Here is Boris, who worked in a foreign Farm before this, with hairy arms and tattooed neck, whose clothes are always impeccably turned out. Orange shirt done up to the very last button. He is in Customs, guiding a plump indie kid girl with dyed red hair over to the office. 'Yes, I'm sure there's no problem at all', he lilts in a reassuring burr. And she smiles. She is reassured. She trusts him. He will fuck her in kind ecstasy in the bright, clean, office. I suspect. Yes, the coffee is good. For us. Perk of the job.

But she may be saved. We can save a few. We save attractive women. Perk of the job.

Don't know how they get here. The air is soft and bright, the sounds are hospital clear. My mind is full of cotton wool. I suspect they are summoned when a ticket lands on a mat. Some have won a competition they never entered. Others get sent on business trips. I am guessing. There is no discrimination on grounds of race, religion, politics. We have full disabled access, well-oiled ramps. This is the twenty-first century. Those who do not turn up for their flight, as far as I know, are left alone. Those who arrive late are turned away and never re-summoned. They are disappointed and remonstrate.

Here comes a black, no a mixed race man, tall, drainpiped by denim, no hand-luggage, agitated and suspicious, looking around him. 'Can I help you, sir?' I sound authoritative, like I won't put up with any nonsense. This man finds it too clean, too efficient, too friendly, I can see. He may not drink coffee. He may be a handful – so I give him a little dirt, a little attitude to make him feel at home, relax out of the perfect. I received no training in this – I came from an agency. I too was selected. If I had not needed the money, taken the job, I wonder if I myself may have received a ticket.

I think there may just be too many people and some need to be skimmed off the top. I think they may be turned into food. I think they may actually be sent to another plane of existence, through the white light that could be the sun blinking off jets, or spaceships, there at the top of the gleaming escalators. There may be something wrong with these people -

Here comes an old white couple, fussing with love, dressed like they were already getting off the plane on the other side.

- that does not possibly show on the surface and justifies it. I think I hope I'm mistaken. I suspect, most darkly, that this entire undertaking may be being carried out simply in order to construct the most efficient and innocent killing facility possible. In other words, that this is all for the sake of the perfect aesthetic of the process.

And having achieved this end, at the last moment, reprieves.

I hope. I think.

Boundary violation

Skarry isn't so much a guardian angel as a piece of virus protection software who sits on my shoulder scanning the world. My psychiatrist insists on referring to him as a 'familiar' and once as an 'imaginary friend'. 'Imaginary fiend!' I blurted out, and shouldn't have done. That was unfair to Skarry, and I could see my psychiatrist's brain throwing up images of Klaus Kinski. But Skarry is a good influence. A calming influence.

He warns me by throwing up Windows with a large red X in them whenever someone means me harm. It first happened when I was watching footage of the G8 summit; multiple windows emerged on the TV all over Tony Blair's face and when George Bush came on talking about debt relief to the sixteen poorest nations there were so many that the TV picture actually slowed down and I swore I could hear it whirring. Then his name echoed in my ears. 'Skarry'. Now, I wasn't that stoned. It was useful. It wasn't frightening; it was what I knew already. I think my psychiatrist was somewhat taken aback when I told him that although I've never actually seen Skarry, my invisible protector, I *know* that he resembles him quite strongly. But Skarry himself has a deformity I can never see. It's that that means he can't emerge into the world and warn the people himself. He has to work through me.

So I tell my psychiatrist about the people Skarry has warned me about. I have a list and hand it over. 'I'm not sure about the spelling of Koizumi', I say. It's crumpled. I should have written it on A4, or typed it, but I don't have a computer and there's too many people in the library. I'm scared the pop-up windows will appear. Sometimes I think I can see them hovering above the heads of people in the distance, in the crowd. I saw the red crosses in David Lammy's eyes when he opened the library and he looked at me for a split second, mouth open. Skarry was telling me I should keep an eye on the library, so I go there every day almost. I can tell the staff suspect I'm stealing books because I don't have a card, but Skarry said not to give them my information, and I take a long and winding route which I change every day when I leave so they don't realise I live so near. I should go in every day, Skarry says, and keep an eye on the library.

'Have you seen any red crosses today?'
'No. But I know they're still there.'
'Mm-hmm. And are there any side-effects from the medication?'
'I feel a little tired. Maybe a little bit down,' I state. The last statement is true.
'You may well feel like that at the beginning. Have you had any thoughts of self-harm?'
I pause then say no. I think I've convinced him. It's simple really; the psychiatrist is a pale copy of Skarry and he can't see behind things into the Truth as Skarry can. He can't read the underlying Code. I have infected him with the Lie Virus by simply reading, learning and reciting the symptoms of the medicine I crush into the toilet and flush, three pills a day.

I consult Skarry in the library, in the poetry section, where no-one goes. I mutter quietly to him beneath the radar. 'What should I do? How do I let the people know?' Now Skarry doesn't physically tell me. That's not his style. But I see the books around me and know which ones those who are ready to find the Truth go for. At home I copy out the lists. The next day I wait until the librarians are busy with a pram and an alarm and stoop down to put the lists in books on Rosicrucians, The Grail and UFOs. Of course, I know any threats these things represented are long-dead or transfigured into the Knights of the electronic age. And there is no overarching conspiracy; they simply mean to do us harm whenever opportunity arises. But the people that read these books are looking for the truth, and I slip a list into each one, near the back, in the books the date stamps indicate have not been taken out for a while. Over the next few days, I memorise their positions and check to see if the lists are still in there. 'Easter eggs', I call them.

I'm not sure I should be telling my psychiatrist everything so I don't tell him about the books. I tell him about the bakery and how I've stopped going because of the way the buns are staring at me. Not literally, I reassure him. It's just the way they're trying to make everyone fat so they can't fight.
'Fight what?'
'I'm not sure exactly, yet. You have to be prepared for every eventuality. They're definitely trying to make us waste the oil on purpose. They've got their own stockpiled, and then they'll sell it to the rich like gold. There won't be any buses. They got rid of the Routemaster because of all this.'

My psychiatrist is a simple computer program, and is easy to outwit.

Happy new year

I was down the Wetherspoons meeting some old friends I wasn't really that arsed about seeing so I arranged to meet them all together and of course they got on a lot better with each other than with me despite the fact they didn't really know each other so I'd gone to the toilet and I was just coming back from the toilet and maybe it was the Rosey Nosey, which was a pound a pint, it being new year now and the bottom of the barrel when I saw an old soak with striated cheeks and more pockmark than nose, a big white beard and a hairless head. 'Oi Father Christmas,' I goaded him, in order to make myself feel better, 'Is this what you do for the rest of the year?' and as his purple-veined face dawned slowly from his chest, its vest, its egg stains and a wet copy of the Sun, he fixed me with his hopeless red eyes in a pitying, withering look that said silently 'Here I am, and here shall you be, in not this exact same place but in this exact same place, when your girlfriend has for the last time left you, when your job has been privatised, when all you can see looking back on the past is the road map to your own self-destruction, here shall you sit, waiting to gaze upon some other young fuck who only hopes he's funny, with this self-same stare, the only gift you can pass on to the world.'

But what his mouth said was 'S-s-sit on my knee, son.'

Guanine

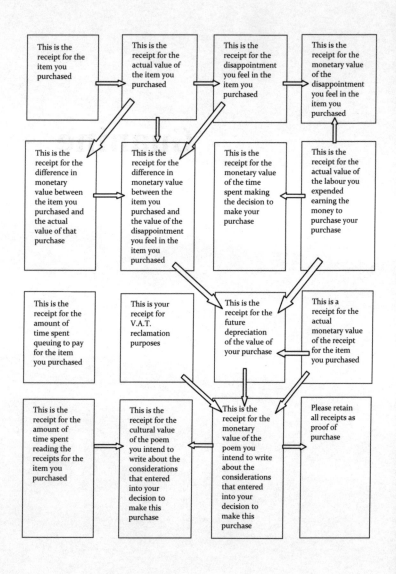

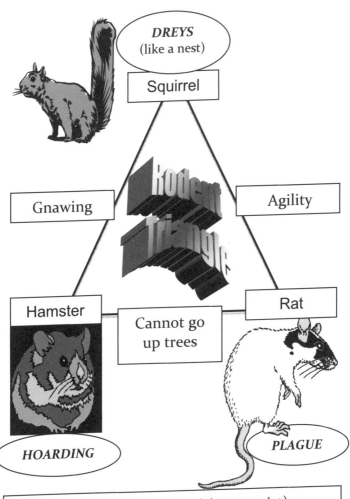

DREYS
(like a nest)

Squirrel

Gnawing

Rodent Triangle

Agility

Hamster

Cannot go
up trees

Rat

HOARDING

PLAGUE

Only three rodents included (more exist)
Duncan still incredulous re: existence of 'dreys'
Rats also possess gnawing teeth
How exactly does this fight racism?
Perhaps consider a Venn diagram.

Tartrazine

If two Hollywood icons of yesteryear were to engage in resource management-based projectile warfare via the use of North American ground-burrowing rodent henchmen

How much of Ed Wood's woodchuck's wood would
Edward Woodward's woodchuck chuck if Edward Woodward's
woodchuck could chuck Ed Wood's woodchuck's wood?

The promise

He said 'I'll make you wish you'd never been born'
and then he put me in a lovely, relaxing womb-like environment
floating in warm Epsom salts.

God's crap Christmas

'I gave my children a brand new religion;
but they only played with the wrapping it came in.'

The celery seller's story

I once was a celery seller on a celery seller's salary
who dwelt inside a cellar with my second sister Valerie
for verily, a celery seller seldom can flee penury
or the smell of celery in his cellarful of celery.

Now, one day they stuck me in a cell for the crime of selling celery
(past its sell-by date) and so they strapped me to the pillory
and merrily, not warily, they pelted me with Dairylea
crying 'silly celery seller, we shall send you to the cemetery!'

But I pushed the pangs of pain into reality's periphery
for nothing, if you summon up the thought of it cerebrally
can surpass the seminal serenity of celery
especially ingested through a smuggled-in suppository.
(Their frisk had been but cursory, a strip-search thought unnecessary.)

So forced to flee the city I sold celery for centuries
my sole peripatetic pal a pottery-peddling peccary
and so we gleaned our calories from celery (and kedgeree)
till, ship-wrecked on the foreshore of a faraway cerulean sea,

We chanced upon a Chancellery, its doors adorned with filigree
in reverie, I sedulously whispered 'Open Sesame'.
Inside it lay this augury: a Penguin rhyming dictionary
containing all the words I'd later use... to rhyme with celery.

Verruca

Recently, I've been beset
by a tenacious medical problem
that attached itself, like a limpet,
to my feet, and tried to nobble 'em.
I've caught a wart, I feel a fool;
I was never taught to wear socks in the pool!
It's big, and round, and angry and red
and it's left me completely snookered -
Oh, can no-one tell me how to rid myself of this verruca?

I've tried to freeze the fucker off with a space-age dildo-bazooka
I tried to burn the bugger up, gas mark five in a pressure cooker
I've tried plasters, I've tried blasters, wasted all my filthy lucre
Oh, can no-one tell me how to rid myself of this verruca?

The battle-scarred sole of my war-torn foot now resembles
mid-nineties Bosnian war battleground Banja Luka
This verruca is a fooker this verruca is not super
Thank God it's vegetarian, it ate my flatmate's yucca
Oh, can no-one tell me how to rid myself of this verruca?

It's grown to over six feet tall; it's now more like a pooka
With me a tiny little dwarf just riding on its shoulder
Perhaps I should get used to it, my girlfriend says 'It suits yer!'
Oh, can no-one tell me how to rid myself of this verruca?

I sacrificed to voodoo gods, I sacrificed a cockerel
I wrote this cathartic poem in a slack lacklustre doggerel
Then one morning as I woke in bed – my foot seemed somehow
lighter
As I drew back the duvet, heart beat faster, fists clenched tighter

Beneath my feet had opened a void where once had been verruca
...and next to me one where my girlfriend had been
– I think the bastard to*ok* her!

So if you should see a beautiful girl a-walking down the street
Arm-in-arm with a flaky, foetid lump of rotting meat
Remember this poem, which, to be honest, will never win me the
                                                              Booker
and tell me where that heartless harlot went, with my verruca!
Oh, can no-one tell me how to rid myself of this verruca?

Look after 'em

To hell with the hound with the hole in his head
guarding the 99p shop's back door
who rounds every purchase back up to a pound
so the blind are led by the poor.

Duck camp

There's a prison at Cockfosters, in the middle of Trent Park
but it's not for Al-Qaeda, or for anarchists or FARC.
It's not built to hold the IRA or Mafioso crooks,
no, it's a suburban internment camp for injured mixed-race ducks...

'That one's got a tiny 'ead!
That one's fevvers're mohican!
That one looks like it's half-seagull,
that one's two-thirds Puerto Rican!
They're like somethin' 'aht of a science-fiction
tale by J.G. Ballard -
who ever 'eard of a black & white-fevvered,
ginger-'eaded mallard?
If we don't keep these foul waterfowl
in the strictest segregation
Their like will muddy the gene pond
of our British ducky nation!

'You can't put 'em down!
You can't send 'em back!
They don't even speak English,
They just go 'Quack! Quack!"

'But look how they're limping,
that's clear evidence of torture!
These guys're the survivors of
internecine goose-duck warfare!
And ok, they can't fly, and
they've all got broken legs,
but they've got something to
contribute to society: EGGS!

We should open the gates,
let them waddle away –
shut down North London's
Guantanimal bay!

'No you can't keep them down!
You can't hold them back!
This is what it sounds like
when ducks cry: 'Quack! Quack!''

I personally have no idea how to proceed.
The issues are all as tangled as pondweed,
but one thing I can state in a trite rhyming couplet
is how we'll *all* take flight to where's best for our ducklings.

So try to keep up!
We're not under attack!
Migration happens,
sure as ducks go 'Quack! Quack!'

There was a young gourmet from Putney
who subsisted entirely on chutney
till, whilst on the subcontinent
he choked on said condiment
which put paid to his chutney gluttony.

There was a prog rock fan from Wolverhampton
who had tickets to see Peter Frampton
but the day before, fell
down a very deep well
and got eaten by the legendary worm of Lambton.

There was a gorilla from Dudley
who was, frankly, incredibly ugly,
and sexually frustrated
till he got fellated
by a zookeeper who found him 'cuddly'.

There was a bum bandit from Lakeside
who would only 'do' folks up the backside
till a corn on the cob
grew out of his knob
from a bit that got caught in his chap's eye.

There was a woman whose surname was Franklin called Aretha
who ate only what came out of her husband's urethra.
Through thus missing her dinner
she grew thinner and thinner
till when held up to the light you could see thru' her.

There was a coprophiliac from Waterloo
who hid under a Glastonbury Portaloo.
He opened his gob
then took out his knob
and tugged on it each time he caught a poo.

There once was a philosopher called Nietzsche
who could come across as a bit of a preacher
but a man beating a horse
drove him mental, of course
because by that stage of his life he was so intellectually estranged
from the tribulations of his fellow man that his sympathies could
only be aroused by the suffering of a dumb, and therefore by his
reasoning innocent,
creature

....or he might have had syphilis.

There was an old man of Heraklion
who was, unsurprisingly, never made the subject of a limerick.

Shit poem

If you're totally teetotal, but abruptly crave some beers,
or to pop out for a Superking, your first in thirty years,
if you wake one afternoon and find you want a wank,
a shag, a spliff, a hit, or a pot noodle, or some crack;

Or should you come round on Hampstead Heath,
head pounding and teeth gnashing,
with no memory whether you went there
for cottaging or gay bashing,
do you feel a sudden urge to listen to Agadoo?
to run out nude into the street and break each last taboo?
or just write a rubbish poem in which
each line rhymes with 'oooh?'
Well, just stop and think before you do
and check you don't just... need... a... poo!

Drown Penfold! Sink the Bismark! Pull a Guinness! Have a shit!
Drop the kids off at the lido! Lose a game of splat the rat!
Launch the penguins, coax the turtle out, pebbledash your cellar!
Strain like you were trying to bend a spoon like Uri Geller!

Or relax, open your sluices, make like a beaver,
build a dam, don't give one, then just press upon the lever.
Ship out a container of rotten bananas!
or shovel a quarter of chocolate sultanas.

Don't leave your wife!
or move to Iraq!
before you've made sure
you don't just need a cack.

O queue for the log flume – but take a sou'wester!
Produce a brown, scaled down Luton town centre!
Crimp out a fudge. If it won't come don't budge
till it has. Let it brew if it must. It won't fester.

Don't become an antisocial round-the-world yachter![1]
until you've given a sea burial to a sea otter...

Yes it's Milk, Milk, Lemonade,
but it's round the corner History's made;
do you think that Adolf Hitler would've planned to invade Britain
if he hadn't had such trouble mit der Schitten?
The Yanks in Vietnam weren't defeated by the VCs,
but by their own psychedelic, Agent Orange-like faeces!
You need a poo, you don't just need a pump!
Plop whoopsy dung crotey turd winnet dump!

Yes this poem is long, and it's crap, and it's sloppy.
I wrote it on the bog in five minutes. I'm sorry.
So wipe carefully! Make sure you got none on your glans,
and do what I'll do with this shite. Wash your hands...

---

[1] Dame Ellen MacArthur

Notes

Notes

Critical switch

Titus Flavius Domitianus (born 24 October AD 51), commonly known as Domitian, was the third and last emperor of the Flavian dynasty, reigning from 14 September 81 to his assassination on 18 September 96.

Roman historians portrayed him as a cruel and paranoid tyrant, but he was so adamant of his love for his wife Domitia Longina he persuaded her first husband to divorce her so that he could marry her himself.

The couple are reported to have had only one child, an unnamed son born in 73 who died sometime around 81. On 24 August 79 Mount Vesuvius erupted, burying the cities of Pompeii and Herculaneum under metres of ash and lava; the following year, a fire broke out in Rome which raged for three days.

Germline

On April 1st 2005, the UK Human Fertilisation and Embryology Authority (www.hfea.gov.uk) introduced legislation which ended the anonymity of sperm donors, who could write a 'goodwill message' to be read by their biological children when they reach the age of eighteen. It also imposed a legal limit of ten biological families to be produced from each donor's sperm (or eggs). There currently exists, however, no limit on numbers provided for export.